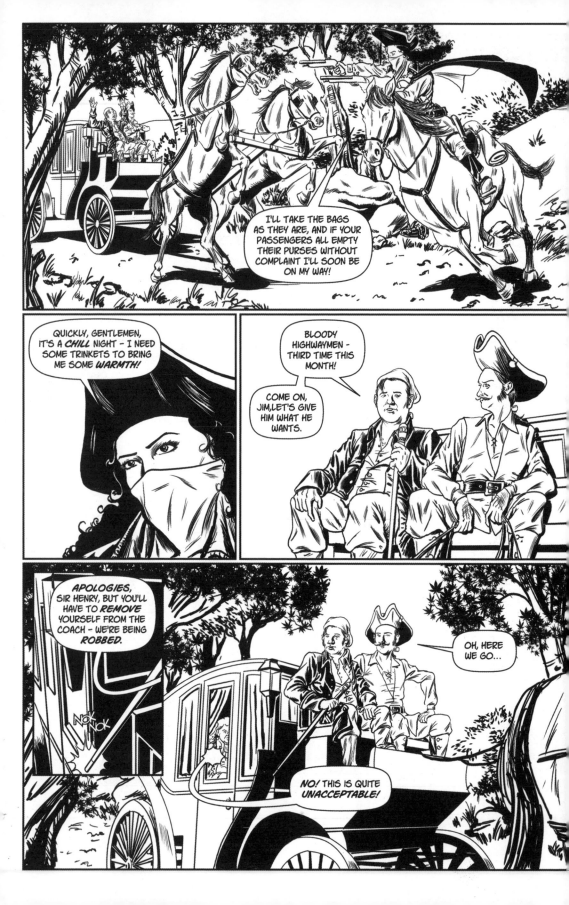

AND A HUMBLE COACHMAN, WHILST A WORTHY FELLOW, IS EASILY BOUGHT.

ARE YOU SUGGESTING THE COACHMEN ARE INVOLVED, WILLIAM? THAT THIS HIGHWAYMAN IS ONE OF THEIR OWN?

I SUGGEST THERE IS *COMPLICITY*, BECAUSE THERE IS *ALWAYS* COMPLICITY - ESPECIALLY WHERE RASCALS ARE CONCERNED.

BUT TO ADDRESS OUR MOST IMMEDIATE CONCERN - SOME HUMBLE COACHMEN OF OUR OWN ARE REQUIRED. SEE TO IT.

FOR MY PART I HAVE *ALREADY* FACILITATED A FORMIDABLE PREDATOR TO BE IN OUR EMPLOY.

YOU SEE, GENTLEMEN, TO *CATCH* A RASCAL WE MUST *THINK* LIKE A RASCAL...

THE INDIAN OCEAN IN THE EIGHTEENTH CENTURY - NOTORIOUS BECAUSE OF THE PIRATES THAT PLUNDER THERE.

IN UNMARKED SHIPS THEY ROAM THE LISTING SEAS, SEARCHING FOR ANY UNFORTUNATE VESSELS THAT MAY HAVE STRAYED FROM THE KNOWN SHIPPING LANES.

WHO KNOWS WHY THOSE FOOLISH SEAFARERS PUT THEMSELVES IN SUCH JEOPARDY - A RASH CAPTAIN, AN INEXPERIENCED CREW OR JUST A CRUEL TWIST OF FATE?

BUT FOR ANY SHIP SPOTTED THROUGH A CUT-THROAT'S LENS THE OUTCOME IS CERTAIN -

shanti
THE PIRATE QUEEN
"A CAPTAIN'S TALE"

WRITTEN BY: STEVE TANNER
ART BY: LORENZO NICOLETTA
LETTERS BY: BOLT-01

- A NASTY FATE FOR ALL THOSE POOR SOULS ABOARD!

HEAVE TO! THEY'RE COMING ALONGSIDE! RECHARGE THAT CANNON!

BOOM

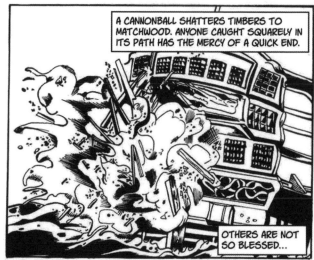

A CANNONBALL SHATTERS TIMBERS TO MATCHWOOD. ANYONE CAUGHT SQUARELY IN ITS PATH HAS THE MERCY OF A QUICK END.

OTHERS ARE NOT SO BLESSED...

MY LEG! I CAN'T FEEL MY LEG!

IT'S GONE, *DICK* – THE BALL TOOK IT. SIT YOURSELF STILL, NOW. SIP SOME OF THIS.

THAT'S IT, YOU'RE FEELING BETTER *ALREADY*, EH?

GOOD LAD, *DICK*, GOOD LAD...

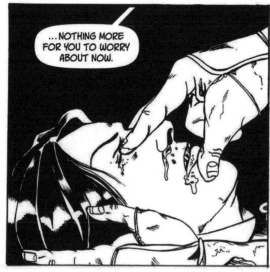

...NOTHING MORE FOR YOU TO WORRY ABOUT NOW.

ABOVE DECKS:

THEY'RE *UPON* US, CAPTAIN! WHAT'S THE *ORDER*?

I... TELL THE CREW TO *STAND DOWN.*

...SIR?

THE MEN UNDER HIS COMMAND ARE NOT A SEASONED FIGHTING CREW - THERE IS ONLY ONE RESPONSE THAT MAY PREVENT BUTCHERY.

TELL THEM!

AND RELAY THAT I WISH TO MAKE PARLEY, BUT WITH GUARANTEE OF CREW SAFETY DURING DISCUSSIONS.

THE CAPTAIN IS QUICKLY TRANSFERRED TO THE PIRATE SHIP TO MAKE HIS PLEAS...

MY NAME IS *CAPTAIN JOHN DICKSON OF THE BLUE BONNET,* LATELY OF PLYMOUTH. OUR SHIP IS A *MERCHANT* VESSEL, LADEN WITH GOODS THAT I KNOW WILL BE OF *LITTLE VALUE* TO YOU.

MAY I KNOW *YOU* AND YOUR *INTENTIONS* TO MY SHIP AND MY CREW?

ON YOUR KNEES, BASTARD! DON'T YOU RECOGNISE ROYALTY WHEN YOU SEE IT?

ROYALTY!? BUT I... FORGIVE ME, MAJESTY! I ASSURE YOU I MEANT NO TRESPASS ON YOUR WATERS!

YET A TRESPASS HAS BEEN MADE...

CAPTAIN, I AM A GOOD QUEEN, CONSIDERED JUST - BUT FOR THE SAKE OF MY CREW I CANNOT LET SUCH AN INSULT GO UNPUNISHED.

MAJESTY, I MEANT NO DISRESPECT! MY VESSEL IS YOURS TO SEARCH, BUT THE BLUE BONNET IS A TRADE SHIP - WE CARRY NO JEWEL OR COIN IN OUR CARGO.

"YOU MISUNDERSTAND ME, CAPTAIN. THE RICHES I DESIRE ARE MORE HUMAN IN NATURE, AND I UNDERSTAND YOU HAVE A HOLD BURSTING WITH THOSE."

BUT THEY'RE JUST SLAVES! THEY'RE OF NO WORTH TO YOU!

I'M NO FOOL, CAPTAIN, BUT THIS IS A FOOL'S ERRAND. IF YOUR CARGO HAS SUCH LITTLE WORTH THEN IT CANNOT BE OF USE TO ANYONE, INCLUDING YOU.

I ACCEPT YOUR TERMS — AND ONE SLAVE, OF MY CHOICE, TO DO WITH AS I WISH.

ONCE I HAVE THAT PRIZE THE REST CAN BE ON THEIR WAY — YOU HAVE MY WORD.

AND SO ONE SLAVE IS SELECTED FROM THE SLAVE VESSEL — A MUSCULAR, AFRICAN MALE WHO HANGS HIS HEAD IN SHAME.

WITH MY COMPLIMENTS, MAJESTY, FOR BEING SO *GRACIOUS* — NOW IF I BE PERMITTED TO *RETURN* TO MY SHIP?

NO. YOU REMAIN *HERE.*

WHAT!? BUT YOU GUARANTEED US SAFE PASSAGE!

NO!

MY MERCY WAS FOR THE BLUE BONNET'S *CARGO* — NOT ITS *CREW.*

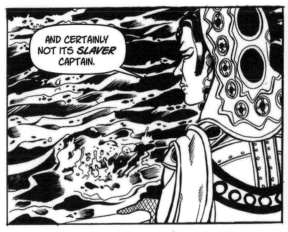

AND CERTAINLY NOT ITS *SLAVER* CAPTAIN.

RELEASE ALL THOSE OTHER POOR WRETCHES FROM THEIR IRONS – THEY CAN TAKE THE SHIP AND DECIDE WHAT THEY WANT TO DO WITH THEIR FORMER CAPTORS.

NOW, WHAT TO DO WITH *YOU*...

The Chirurgery

Chi•rur'ger•y noun [See Chirurgeon , and confer Surgery .] Surgery. [Obsolete]

The Flintlock Chirurgery is intended to be a closer look at some of the historical events, inspirations and reasonings behind our Eighteenth Century tales; the taking of a scalpel to our body of stories and peeling back their layers for closer examination of the facts that drive the fictions...

"THE HIGHWAYMEN DIDN'T ALL TAKE THEIR LEAVE ONCE DICK TURPIN DROPPED AT YORK, YOU KNOW!"

*T*hey certainly didn't, but my previous comics associated with that notorious highwayman did suggest to some that Flintlock would feature Mr Turpin with some prominence and I offer apologies right up front that the world's most well-known highway robber is missing from these pages.

Flintlock was never planned to be a showcase for Dick Turpin, but it's clear from our opening Lady Flintlock tale that his exploits and fate are well-known. He was the career criminal of the age, so his infamy is understandable a relatively short time after he was hung at York in 1739.

It remains to be seen (or should that be revealed) whether Turpin's notoriety has any bearing on Sarah Flintlock's own decision to don the mask and load the pistols herself. Certainly Turpin exists in the Flintlock timeline, and it would be relatively easy to shoe-horn my previous Dick Turpin stories into that chronology, but I really am undecided whether the Turpin who did drop at York is more the historical figure or my own brutally anti-heroic interpretation. I think it probably best to leave it at that for now.

What is clear cut, however, is that highway robbery thrived right through the 18th Century and (whilst not considered an acceptable career path) attracted a fair share of men and women hoping to take some easy pickings of other folk's possessions. It really was not a gender –specific occupation, although very few women who decided to become highwaymen dressed in a way that would reveal their sex.

(Interjection: I'll be using the words highwayman/ highwaymen within and without of these pages to describe Lady Flintlock and her contemporaries. Just so you know.)

Some carried that through into their daily life, with many female robbers dressing in male clothing routinely. The most well-known of these would be Moll Cutpurse, who was already nearly 100 years dead by 1751 when Lady Flintlock's story begins.

Moll, real name Mary Frith, may not have been an inspiration or even known to the women that followed her, but she is now historically regarded as the first of the female highway robbers despite the fact that most of her crimes were conducted on foot rather than horseback.

A tomboy from an early age, Moll mixed well in the company of both men and women and after running away to London became first a successful pickpocket and then a respected fence (handler of stolen goods) in the lower society of the City, going on to achieve a respected notoriety amongst higher society as well.

So great was her fame she even had a play written about her – "The Roaring Girl" – which was written by Thomas Middleton & Thomas Dekker and first performed in 1611. A surviving fronts-piece of the play published at the time can be seen opposite.

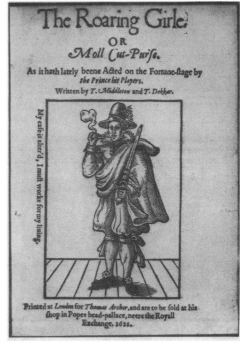

When Moll decided to turn to highway robbery as another means of income she did that in style too – levelling her pistol at none other than General Thomas Fairfax, a leading Parliamentary commander in the English Civil war. She relieved Fairfax of a considerable purse of gold before shooting him in the arm and fleeing back to London, and all this in broad daylight.

Her brazenness was her undoing and the recognisable Moll was soon identified and captured, but the spoils from her previous exploits allowed her to buy her freedom at for the then small fortune of £2000!

By the time the Eighteenth Century arrived the female highwayman was firmly established.

Sarah Davis outlived her two highwayman partners that she robbed with as a willing accomplice. Born in Cripplegate, London, in 1685, she was seduced by James Wadsworth in her early teens and became his decoy. After Wadsworth was hung in 1702, she soon fell in with another knight of the road nicknamed Norwich Will but barely 6 months later he had also felt the noose tighten.

Perhaps this was enough to make Sarah reconsider her options, for she abandoned highway robbery and turned to petty theft.

It was too little, too late – Sarah was arrested for shoplifting in Clerkenwell and at twenty years old was hung at Tyburn on Friday 13th July, 1705.

Mary Blacket was hung at Tyburn in 1726 for highway robbery, although protested her innocence throughout. Her insistence that hers was a case of mistaken identity continued right to the gallows, where she met her fate without a trace of fear.

In the latter half of the 18th Century one convicted highway robber, Mary Pyle, avoided the traditional meeting with the hangman – and records reveal that she was one of the first convicts sent from England to Botany Bay in 1785.

But any brief summary of female highwaymen would be lacking without mention of the most notorious and well-known.

Lady Katherine Ferrers becoming very famous for her exploits in the latter half of the Seventeenth Century. Ferrers was married young to an elderly wealthy land-owner, and turned to highway robbery for no other reason than to alleviate her boredom.

Disguising herself and using a secret passageway from her bedroom, Ferrers robbed for fun along the stretch of road that ran outside her house. Incensed by this mysterious highwayman that was soon regularly accosting travellers in the vicinity of his own home, a reward of £50 for his capture was offered by none other than the elderly Lord Ferrers himself.

Her most famous moonlight encounter was with Jerry Jackson – another highwayman who pulled his own pistol when faced with hers. Forcing her to unmask Jackson discovered Ferrers' true gender during that encounter and they became both partners in love and crime until Jackson was hung at Tyburn.

Of all the female highwaymen the image of Ferrers is the one that has endured through the centuries, her striking looks, swashbuckling style and well-born background capturing the imagination. The 1945 movie The Wicked Lady starring Margaret Lockwood was based on her life, which was a blockbuster of its day. The 1983 remake is not so highly regarded, and was critically mauled on release, but still testament to the enduring appeal of all the Wicked Ladies of the road!

Lady Katherine Ferrers

"SO WE BEST KEEP OUR HEADS DOWN AND AVOID MISTER FIELDING'S LOT"

In 1749, fuelled by the rising tide of crime in London and the failings of the justice system in successfully prosecuting criminals, Henry Fielding created the Bow Street Runners.

Originally numbering just eight men, they have since become regarded as London's first professional police force. Fielding was already well-known by the time he formed the Runners. A dramatist and novelist (Tom Jones is his most famous work, first published in 1749) Fielding was also a magistrate attached to the courts at Bow Street, highly regarded in the city for his efforts to achieve judicial reform and improve prison conditions, and it was his standing and reputation that enabled him to form the Runners.

Fielding's group of constables and ex constables differed to the existing policing methods in being the first group of law-enforcers in the city who were a formal body; their official attachment to the Bow Street magistrates office presenting them as an official, regularised organisation to the public.

This was important, as although unofficial thief-takers (men who would charge a fee to solve petty crimes) were commonplace these men and their methods were routinely considered to be corrupt.

The Bow Street Runners were based at Fielding's house in Bow Street, and they were tasked with locating and arresting serious offenders. As part of their duties they were also entitled to claim any official rewards that resulted in prosecution and conviction. Although this also made them essentially thief-takers too, Fielding hoped that his oversight of them would maintain their respectability and avoid the corruption accusations and general distrust.

This was only partly successful, however, since many were former thief-takers and the runners needed connections in the criminal underworld in order to successfully identify and apprehend suspects.

Over time, however, they became more respectable, and respected.

Initially Fielding obtained money from the government to pay them. However, this soon ran dry and unable to secure any more funding the Bow Street Runners and their services were widely advertised in newspapers.

When Henry Fielding died in 1754, his brother John took over the stewardship of the runners. John Fielding, blinded in an accident when he was 19, was also a magistrate with the nickname of "The Blind Beak" – and a reputation that he could identify a criminal from their voice alone.

John introduced a register for all crimes to be recorded and lists of stolen goods, as well as introducing foot patrols around the wider parts of the city, and of course under his tenure there were now much more than eight runners available to police London.

By the close of the Eighteenth Century the Bow Street Runners had become a full-time police force, made up of a body of experienced men respected by the general public and feared by those who committed the crimes the runners were there to prevent.

Sources:
The English Highwayman by Peter Haining
Stand and Deliver! by David Brandon
www.londonlives.org

Back Matter

As part of the pre-publicity for Flintlock, a brief interview with me featured in some well-respected British comics news blogs. It outlines my reasonings behind what I am trying to achieve with Flintlock quite nicely, so I thought I would reprint it here with added commentary where I felt it appropriate.

Since 2007 Time Bomb Comics has been publishing critically acclaimed one-shots and graphic novels. A regular exhibitor on the booming comics convention circuit, the public face of Time Bomb Comics is Steve Tanner who, with his passion for the medium and penchant for garishly patterned jackets, is the driving force behind the Birmingham based Indie publisher.

Now, nearly ten years on, Tanner has decided to do something different through Time Bomb Comics that marks a step-change for the brand by creating and publishing what is intended to be an ongoing title: Flintlock. "I'm describing it as adventures in the eighteenth century!" he enthuses. He explains that the book will be a shared timeline anthology that features regular and rotating characters – and each story in Flintlock will take place at some point between 1701 and 1800. He reveals that he has created a number of original characters who will make their debut throughout the series, including pirates, rogues, samurai, law enforcers and highwaymen.

In fact, there are six characters who will make their debut in their own stories over the first six books. I've a creative need to kick back against the abundance of characters who are cut from the same cloth. The traditional action hero is almost invariably a 25 - 35 year old white heterosexual male - and that character template seems such a well trodden path! So none of the six debut characters will fall in line with that tradition, even though one or two may appear to do so at first glance. The closest we have in our first book to the stereotypical white male hero is The Clockwork Cavalier – a cold, emotionless, emasculated automaton. Make of that what you will!

The shared timeline also warrants a little further explanation. All the characters we meet co-exist within the 100 year span, but that doesn't mean that they will themselves ever meet one another in any meaningful or significant way. However what one character does in one story may have a significant impact on the actions of another – sometimes even decades apart. There'll be some foreshadowing in place for some of this, and I'll throw out the nugget that at least one other of the six core characters has also made their debut in Flintlock Book One. At the same time not everything will be signposted because, well, I like surprises – don't you?

Both Steve Tanner and Time Bomb Comics first became known to many for the historical horror mash-ups featuring the eighteenth century highwayman Dick Turpin, so will Flintlock just be offering more of the same?

"Well, the era is the same!" Tanner admits. "Researching the Dick Turpin stories really opened my eyes as to how rich the Eighteenth Century is as a setting, and sparked off for me a real fascination with the period. I used to think it was the boring bit between the middle ages and the Victorians – how wrong I was! Part of that may be that we still only really see the 18th Century distilled through the novels of Jane Austen and the like. Beyond that there's a world in transformation with some wonderful opportunities to tell some good stories. That said, the opportunity to create a unique highwayman character as part of the Flintlock universe was too good to pass up – and Lady Flintlock is very different to my take on Dick Turpin!"

"Actually, the first two stories that feature in Flintlock Book 1 have female leads. As well as Lady Flintlock we have Shanti the Pirate Queen. Shanti is Asian – from India – very different from the traditional pirate. There's so few Indian Asian characters in British comics so I'm interested to see how she's received."

I've since been informed that there aren't any at all in British comics, but I do find that incredibly hard to believe. I don't mean supporting cast, but lead characters in their own strip, and admittedly off the top of my head I can't think of any. However, please let me know if that's not the case as I'd be delighted to share the details of them.

Over the last 9 years Tanner has evolved Time Bomb Comics from what was essentially a platform to promote his own work into something more far reaching with a wide range of creators featured in a diverse range of titles. But why would a small publisher known for producing one-shots and graphic novels suddenly embark on something perhaps considered more ambitious?

"The last full comic I wrote for Time Bomb was Dick Turpin and the Crimson Plague back in 2011. Since then I've been fortunate to publish some great books featuring some great creators – including some who inspired me to start up Time Bomb in the first place – but I wanted an opportunity to wear my grand Creator hat again,which to be honest had been lying forgotten in the corner gathering dust."

But although Tanner has written the stories himself, he has recruited some talented artists to help him tell them. United States creator Anthony Summey is the artist on Lady Flintlock and brings a clean, classic style ideally suited to adventure storytelling. He's no stranger to Time Bomb or the subject matter either, having a short story in the 2015 Bomb Scares horror anthology. Also on board is newcomer Lorenzo Nicoletta, the artist for Shanti the Pirate Queen, and marks the first UK comics appearance for the Italian creator. Ed Machiavello has drawn The Clockwork Cavalier, his exquisitely detailed and researched artwork raising eyebrows further when you realise that he lives and works in Uruguay. Finally, another Bomb Scares alumni – Bolt-01 - is the letterer.

Comics are nothing without collaboration, and the creators that have joined with me to produce the Flintlock series will be properly spotlighted here in future books!

Time Bomb Comics successfully released Bomb Scares in October last year using Kickstarter the crowd-funding platform is being used again as a pre-order opportunity for Flintlock Book One.

The Kickstarter pre-order was really successful, so much so that the inclusion of The Clockwork Cavalier in Book One (a character debut originally planned for Book Two) and our format for each book is entirely due to set stretch goals being achieved. Future books in the series will also have a pre-order Kickstarter campaign prior to publication, so watch out for them.

Finally, I really hope you've enjoyed this first book in the Flintlock series - let me know using the contact details above.

Cheers!

Steve Tanner, Creator